For information regarding permission, write to:
Disney Licensed Publishing, 114 Fifth Avenue, New York, New York 10011.

0-7172-7761-5
Printed in the U.S.A.
First printing, November 2006

Disney · PIXAR

THE INCREDIBLES

SCHOLASTIC INC.

New York   Toronto   London   Auckland   Sydney
Mexico City   New Delhi   Hong Kong   Buenos Aires

Not so long ago, an elite group of heroes used their special powers to protect innocent citizens from harm. They were the Supers. Among them were Frozone, Gazerbeam, and Elastigirl.

But one of the Supers stood out from the rest. His name was Mr. Incredible. He was the most popular hero in the city, though he insisted on working alone.

One day, Buddy—Mr. Incredible's number-one fan—showed up at a bank robbery wearing a pair of rocket boots to help him fly. Mr. Incredible simply said, "Fly home, Buddy. I work alone."

But Buddy didn't listen. Mr. Incredible managed to save Buddy from a bomb, but a bank robber escaped, some train tracks were destroyed, and a few people were hurt. It was after that day that the Supers' lives changed forever. . . .

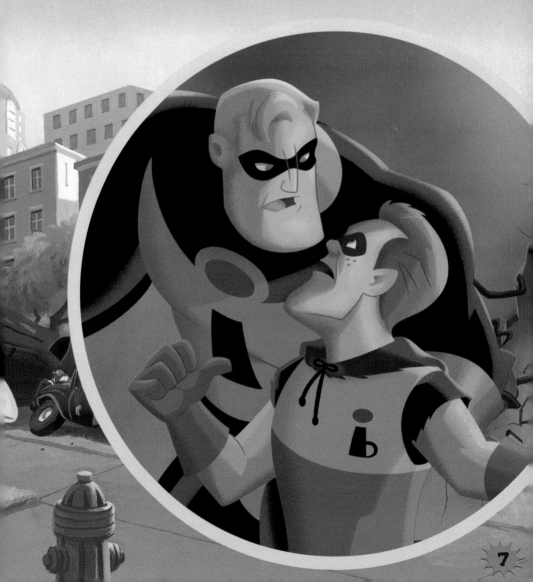

People started to think Supers did more harm than good. The government decided that Supers should no longer be allowed to use their powers. So Mr. Incredible and his new bride, Elastigirl, became known as Bob and Helen Parr to the rest of the world.

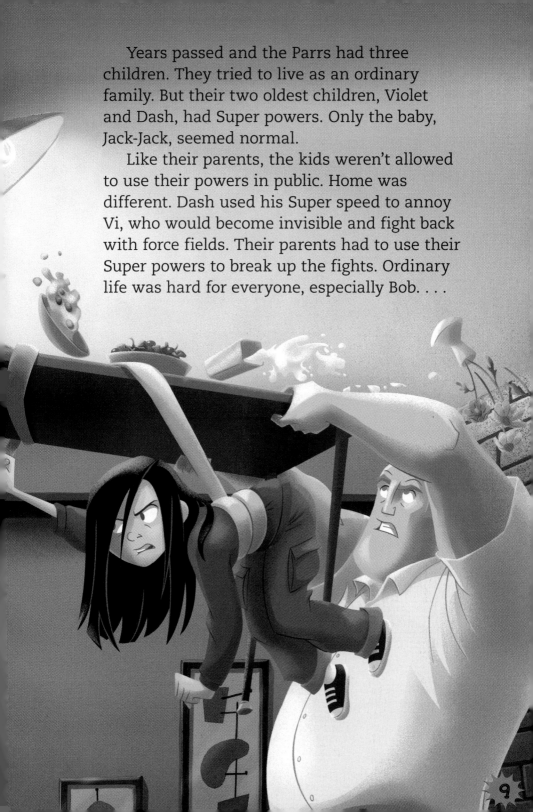

Years passed and the Parrs had three children. They tried to live as an ordinary family. But their two oldest children, Violet and Dash, had Super powers. Only the baby, Jack-Jack, seemed normal.

Like their parents, the kids weren't allowed to use their powers in public. Home was different. Dash used his Super speed to annoy Vi, who would become invisible and fight back with force fields. Their parents had to use their Super powers to break up the fights. Ordinary life was hard for everyone, especially Bob. . . .

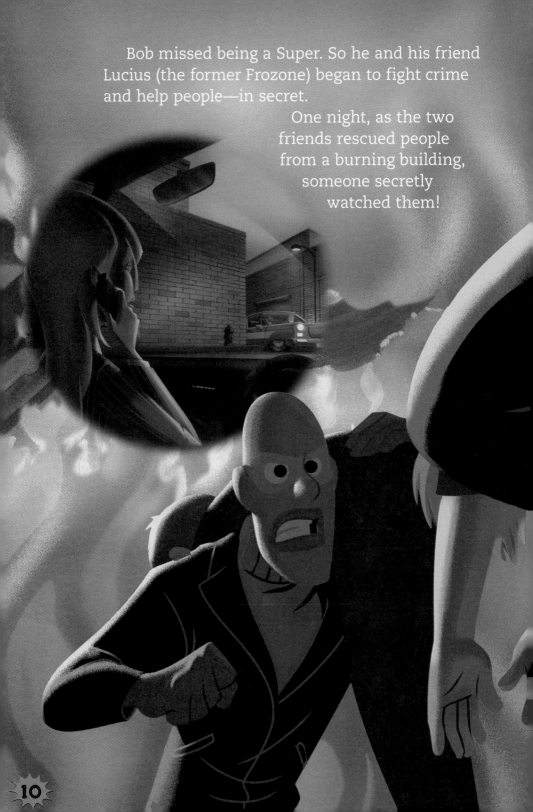

Bob missed being a Super. So he and his friend Lucius (the former Frozone) began to fight crime and help people—in secret.

One night, as the two friends rescued people from a burning building, someone secretly watched them!

10

A mysterious woman named Mirage followed Bob and Lucius and then told her boss about them. Mr. Incredible was just the person Mirage and her boss had been looking for.

The next day, Bob was fired from his everyday job after a particularly rough day with his boss. When Bob came home, he found a small computer in his briefcase. The screen lit up.

"Hello, Mr. Incredible," Mirage said. "I represent a top-secret division of the government . . . and we have need of your unique abilities."

Mirage said the government needed Bob's help to stop an out-of-control experimental robot. "The Supers aren't gone, Mr. Incredible. You're still here," she finished. Then her message self-destructed.

Bob accepted the mission. He did not tell his family he had been fired . . . again. Instead, he told them he was going on a business trip.

Within hours, Mr. Incredible was on a jet heading for the island of Nomanisan.

Mirage described the mission. "The Omnidroid 9000 is a top-secret, battle-prototype robot," she explained. "We lost control of it and now it's loose in the jungle." She warned Mr. Incredible that the robot would quickly learn his moves. The hero was to defeat the expensive Omnidroid without destroying it.

"Shut it down. Do it quickly. Don't destroy it," Mr. Incredible summed up his task.

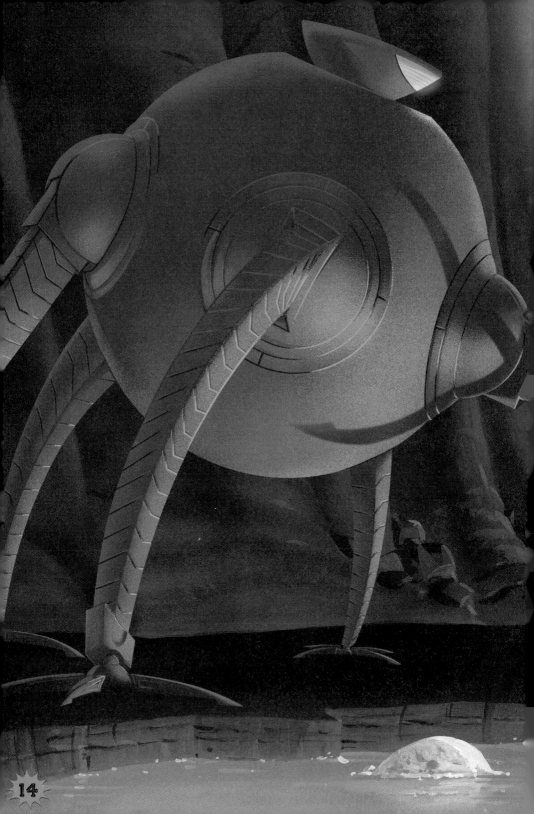

14

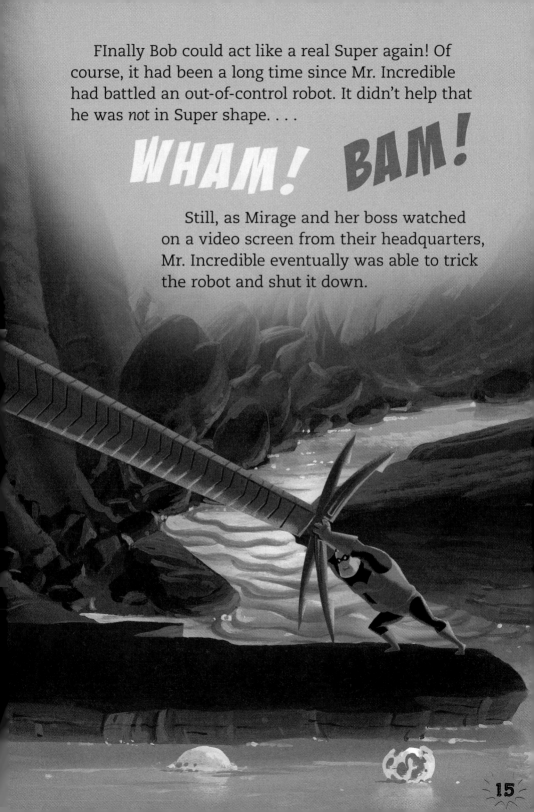

FInally Bob could act like a real Super again! Of course, it had been a long time since Mr. Incredible had battled an out-of-control robot. It didn't help that he was *not* in Super shape. . . .

WHAM! BAM!

Still, as Mirage and her boss watched on a video screen from their headquarters, Mr. Incredible eventually was able to trick the robot and shut it down.

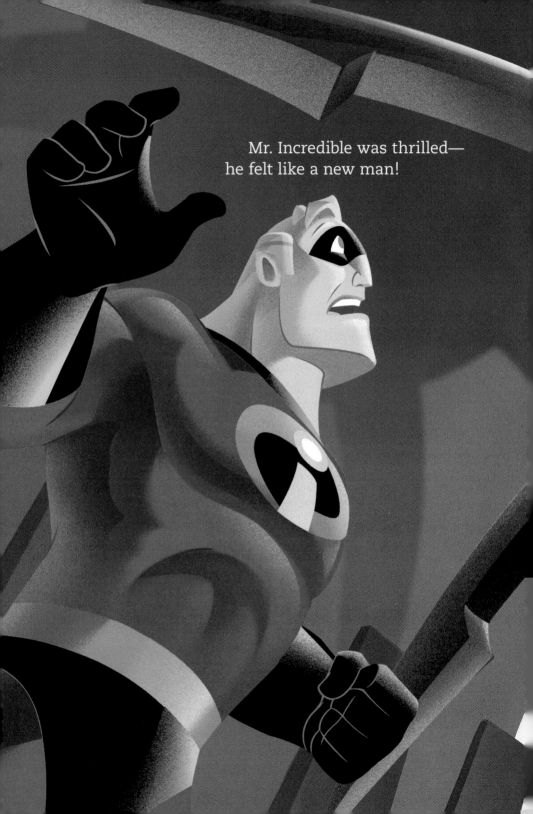

Mr. Incredible was thrilled—
he felt like a new man!

Back at home, he started a new routine. Each day, he pretended to go to work, but instead, Mr. Incredible exercised. Soon he was as fit and as strong as his old Super self!

He even had a new Super suit made by Edna Mode, former designer for the Supers. When Mirage called again, Mr. Incredible was ready. Following her instructions, he flew back to the island of Nomanisan.

Once again, he battled an Omnidroid. But this Omnidroid was much faster and stronger—and smarter! It anticipated all of Mr. Incredible's moves, eventually capturing Mr. Incredible!

Suddenly Mr. Incredible heard a wild laugh! "It's bigger! It's badder! It's finally ready," yelled a wild-haired man who jetted down to face the captured Super. He looked familiar.

"Buddy?" asked the amazed Mr. Incredible.

"My name is *not* Buddy! And it's not Incrediboy, either," shrieked the bitter, grown-up Buddy. "All I wanted to do was help you. . . . But I learned an important lesson: you can't count on anyone!"

"Now I have a weapon that only I can defeat," he added, laughing evilly. "I'm Syndrome!" Syndrome tossed Mr. Incredible over a cliff, into the river below.

Then Syndrome threw a bomb into the water to get rid of the Super for good.

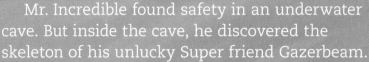

Mr. Incredible found safety in an underwater cave. But inside the cave, he discovered the skeleton of his unlucky Super friend Gazerbeam.

Fortunately for Mr. Incredible, though, Gazerbeam's skeleton blocked the probe Syndrome had sent after him. Gazerbeam had also left a clue, carving the word KRONOS into the cave wall before he died.

Mr. Incredible escaped from the cave. Then he found his way to Syndrome's headquarters and the villain's main computer.

When Mr. Incredible typed the word KRONOS into the computer, Syndrome's plan appeared! There was a long list of Supers—and most of them were listed as TERMINATED. It quickly became clear that Syndrome had been using Supers to train his Omnidroid. Now that Syndrome had perfected the robot, he was going to launch the Omnidroid against the city.

Suddenly Mr. Incredible's suit started beeping. Mr. Incredible didn't know why, but he did know it was time to run. Before he could escape, though, sticky globs shot from wall-mounted guns surrounded and captured him.

23

The beeping came from a homing device that Edna Mode had sewn into Mr. Incredible's Super suit. Helen had activated it after meeting with Edna.

Edna Mode had also made Super suits for the rest of the Parr family.

Helen decided to go and find Bob. Unfortunately, as Helen was trying to tell Vi to take care of her brothers while she was gone, Dash found the kids' new Super suits. He raced around in his Super-speedy suit. When Vi tried out hers, she learned that her suit turned invisible when she did.

"Hey, both of you! Knock it off!" Helen cried.

Soon Elastigirl had everything under control. She boarded a jet bound for Nomanisan. But as the jet neared the island, Elastigirl discovered Violet and Dash on board! They quickly blamed each other for stowing away.

"You left Jack-Jack alone?" Elastigirl cried.

"Of course we got a sitter! Do you think I'm totally irresponsible?" asked Vi.

Elastigirl phoned the sitter, but the call was cut short. The jet was under attack!

27

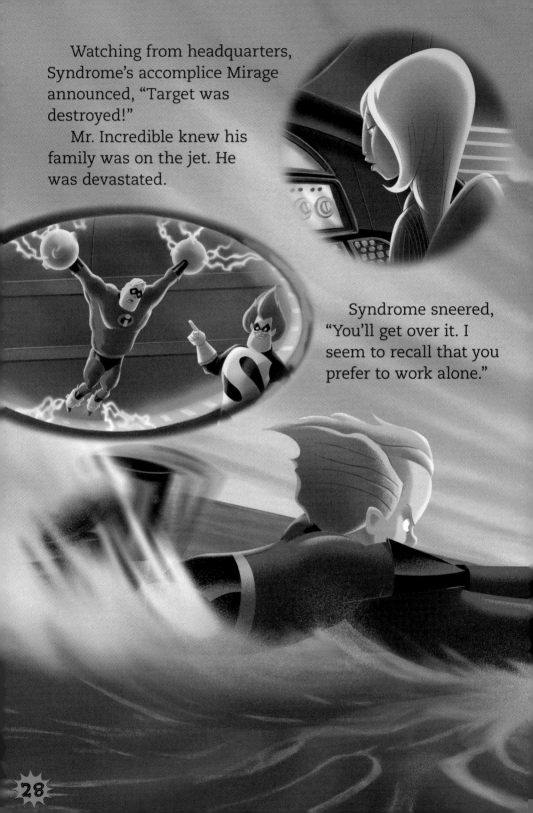

Watching from headquarters, Syndrome's accomplice Mirage announced, "Target was destroyed!"

Mr. Incredible knew his family was on the jet. He was devastated.

Syndrome sneered, "You'll get over it. I seem to recall that you prefer to work alone."

But Syndrome had
underestimated Elastigirl.
She had made herself into
a parachute and landed with
the children safely in the ocean.
Then Elastigirl had shaped herself
into a boat. Using Dash's Super-fast
legs as a motor, the Super family
raced towards the island to
rescue Mr. Incredible!

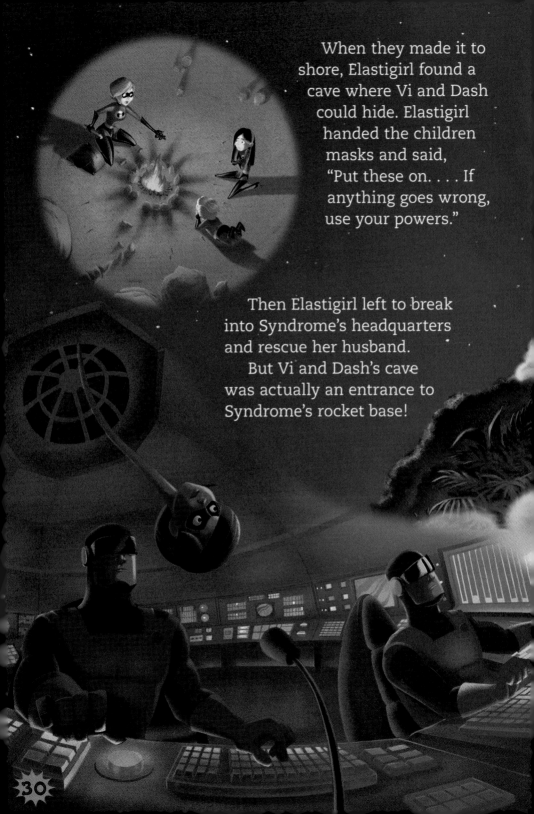

When they made it to shore, Elastigirl found a cave where Vi and Dash could hide. Elastigirl handed the children masks and said, "Put these on. . . . If anything goes wrong, use your powers."

Then Elastigirl left to break into Syndrome's headquarters and rescue her husband. But Vi and Dash's cave was actually an entrance to Syndrome's rocket base!

Soon after, a giant fireball forced Vi and
Dash out of their cave. The fireball turned out
to be the rocket exhaust from Syndrome's base.
Dash and Vi watched as the rocket carrying
the Omnidroid rocketed into the night sky and
headed toward the city.

The next morning, Dash spotted what
he thought was a talking bird. It was one of
Syndrome's security alerts! Suddenly Vi and
Dash were surrounded by guards!

"Remember what Mom said," Violet whispered. "Run!" Dash ran, and Vi turned invisible.

Meanwhile, Elastigirl found Mr. Incredible with Mirage and gave her a swift punch. He started to explain that Mirage had switched sides and was helping him to escape, but there was no time!

Mirage announced that Syndrome had sent his guards after Vi and Dash! Quickly Mr. Incredible and Elastigirl raced to rescue their children.

Mr. Incredible and Elastigirl
reached the jungle. Suddenly
a big, round force field rolled
through the trees with Violet
and Dash inside.

KLONK!

"Mom! Dad!" cried Violet. Their reunion was
cut short as Syndrome's guards surrounded
them. Working together, the Incredibles made an
incredible team. But they were on Syndrome's turf.
Soon the villain caught them in his immobi-ray!

Back at his headquarters, Syndrome told the captive family his plans. He had already sent the Omnidroid to the city. "The robot will emerge dramatically and do some damage. Just when all hope is lost, Syndrome will save the day! I'll be a bigger hero than you ever were!"

Then Syndrome left to "save" the city, leaving the Incredibles behind.

Meanwhile, the Omnidroid was already ripping through the city. The people were terrified. Then Syndrome arrived to save the day. "Stand back!" he shouted. He secretly used his remote control, and the Omnidroid's arm fell off.

The crowd went wild, cheering for Syndrome. His plan was working. Syndrome looked like a hero!

But Syndrome had made a huge mistake. Because the robot was capable of learning, the Omnidroid quickly figured out that Sydrome was using a remote control.

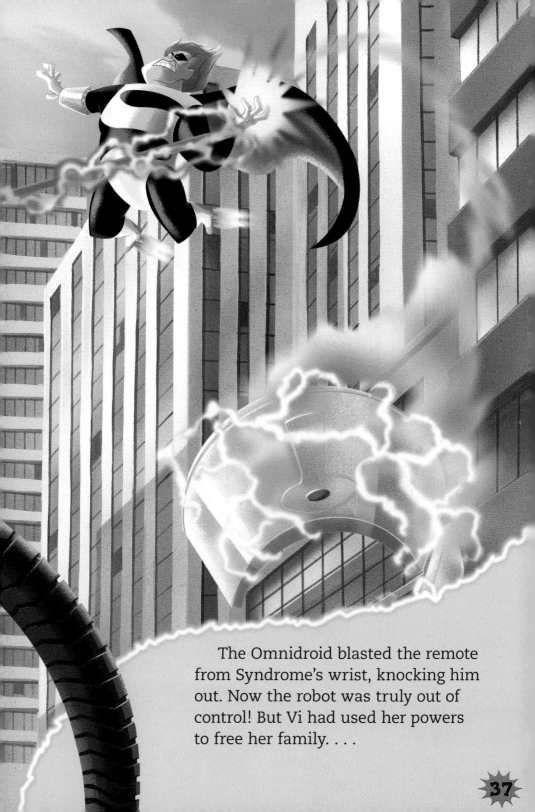

The Omnidroid blasted the remote
from Syndrome's wrist, knocking him
out. Now the robot was truly out of
control! But Vi had used her powers
to free her family. . . .

The Incredibles raced to the city on one of Syndrome's rockets. When they arrived, Mr. Incredible told his family he was going after the Omnidroid alone. At first, Elastigirl was upset. Then Bob blurted out, "I can't lose you again! I'm not strong enough."

Surprised and touched Elastigirl replied gently, "If we work together, you won't have to be."

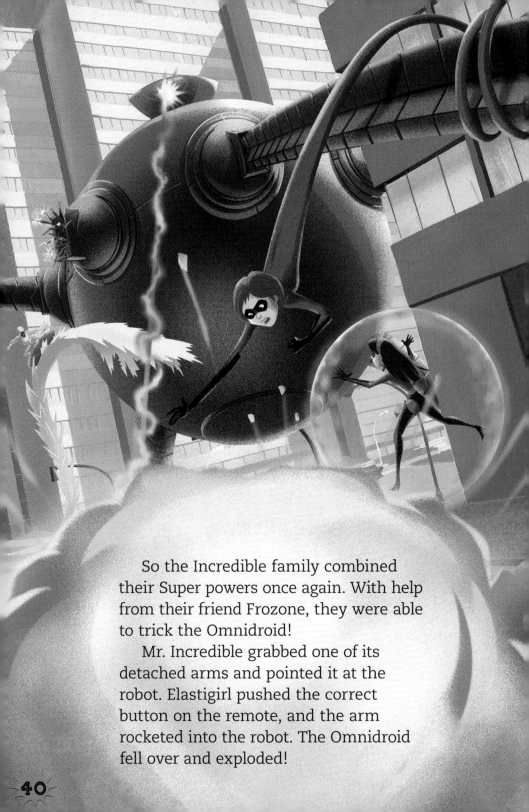

So the Incredible family combined their Super powers once again. With help from their friend Frozone, they were able to trick the Omnidroid!

Mr. Incredible grabbed one of its detached arms and pointed it at the robot. Elastigirl pushed the correct button on the remote, and the arm rocketed into the robot. The Omnidroid fell over and exploded!

41

The Supers had won! They had destroyed the Omnidroid. The crowd cheered.

But the Incredible family's problems weren't over. Syndrome wanted revenge. When the Parrs arrived home, they found that Syndrome had kidnaped Jack-Jack!

The Incredible family sprang into action as Syndrome blasted up to his jet.

Fortunately, it turned out that Jack-Jack had Super powers, too! He turned into a monster!

Frightened, Syndrome dropped the baby in midair. Mr. Incredible threw Elastigirl, who quickly caught Jack-Jack. Then she turned herself into a parachute, and mother and son floated down.

Syndrome wasn't so lucky. His cape got tangled in the jet's turbine, causing the plane to explode. The Incredibles had seen Syndrome for the last time.

It was not the last time the Incredibles would face danger. But from then on, they no longer had to hide their powers—at least not all the time.

They really were a Super family.

EYE SPY

Have your own **SUPER** mission. Look back in the story and try to find these incredible pictures.